DON'T GO WHERE I CAN'T FOLLOW

FIRST PRINTING 2006
ALL CONTENTS © ANDERS NILSEN
PUBLISHED BY DRAWN AND QUARTERLY (PETITS LIVRES)
P.O. BOX 48056 MONTREAL, QUEBEC, CANADA H2V 4S8
www.drawnandquarterly.com
PRODUCTION: ANDERS NILSEN
PUBLISHER: CHRIS OLIVEROS
PUBLICITY: PEGGY BURNS
PRINTED IN CANADA

Don't Go Where I Can't Follow

by Anders Nilsen

For Cheryl

Drawn and Quarterly 2006

1. Postcards from her to him

artist statement:

I know this boy
named anders.

He makes my heart
ache and my stomach
flutter.

cheryl weaver
september, 2000

So, next time you're speeding
Honk and wave when you race by.

Honk and wave.

*Ebony
jewelwing*

USA 33

anders nilsen
2867 milwaukee ave
chicago, Il 60618

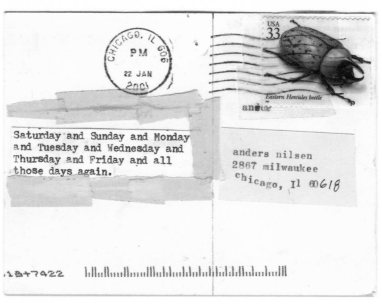

Saturday and Sunday and Monday
and Tuesday and Wednesday and
Thursday and Friday and all
those days again.

Eastern Hercules beetle

USA 33

anders nilsen
2867 milwaukee
chicago, Il 60618

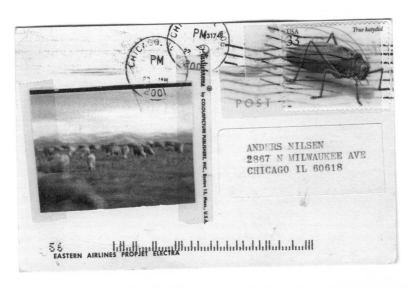

ANDERS NILSEN
2867 N MILWAUKEE AVE
CHICAGO IL 60618

EASTERN AIRLINES PROPJET ELECTRA

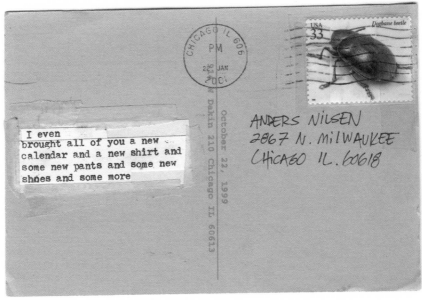

I even
brought all of you a new
calendar and a new shirt and
some new pants and some new
shoes and some more

ANDERS NILSEN
2867 N. MILWAUKEE
CHICAGO IL. 60618

2. The Camping Trip

Dear Ella

HELLO!

(Hmm, that kind of
writing looks spooky
but it's not supposed
to be spooky - it's
supposed to be
Festive!)

How are you? Is Cici around
yet? Is ~~this~~ summer vacation
treating you right? Been to the
Maine shore yet? Echo Lake?

I've been to the lake. It was a
disaster. It should have been a
three stooges movie. Only there were
only two stooges, me and Cheryl.
(although one of the raccoons could
have qualified) Here's the story: Sorry it
got kind of long... Just be glad you didn't live thru it.

        SO...

Get this
story from
Cici and
Dad's
letters

Cheryl was going out of town
and we wanted to do something
nice before she left so we decided
to go camping. We borrowed a
friend's tent and set out for a
spot on Lake Michigan. It's near
a town called Luddington, on the
western coast of the State of
Michigan. We wanted to go there
because we ~~kno~~ had been there
two years ago, and ~~knew it~~

①

would be beautiful and there wouldn't
be too many people. It is a
beach that you have to park your
car about two miles away from, and
hike in, on a sandy path through
the forest and over big hills.
i'm going to tell the story as a
series of episodes, titled for the
Thing in each that WENT WRONG!

remember
this expression? if not
ask Ulla.

The Alarm:

→ uffda meg! It was HOT
in Chicago the day before we left.
we don't have air conditioning so
we turned on the fan. I got home
from work late that night, we
turned on the fan and set the alarm
for 5:00 am. we wanted to get
up early to avoid traffic and
to ensure that we got to the
camping spot before the sun
got too hot, baking us in the
car. we went to sleep for a
while but both slept restlessly,
between the heat and the

②

Fan I was getting dried out
like a little raisin. Finally at
about 4:30 am I woke up and,
bleary eyed, tried to push the
fan away. I was tired and
not super-coordinated. I struggled
for a while and finally got it
propped just right, then went back
to sleep (I think I got up and
peed and got a glass of water too.
~~this time~~ I slept again for what
felt like about 10 or 20 minutes
and rolled over to see what time it
was. IT WAS 7:00! In moving the
fan, I had dislodged the plug for
the alarm and we had overslept.
Groggy (though better ~~re~~sted than
we wo_uld_ have been) and a little
grumpy, we packed the car and
hit the road

THE FLIES

Miraculously, we didn't get lost on
the way to Luddington (last year
we were half way to detroit when

we realized we were off the
right road). We still made good
time and arrived at the
parking lot in the forest at
around noon. I had worked all
weekend and Cheryl had driven
most of the day. ~~there was~~
we were both looking forward ~~to~~
with Great anticipation to
lounging on the beach, maybe swimming
and reading, but doing ABSOLUTELY
NOTHING if possible. A lot of
laying around sounded great. So
we parked, loaded up our backpacks
and set out on the sandy two
mile hike to the beach. We got
there in pretty good time, despite
our lethargy, and found a nice
spot for the tent, up a hill (a sand
dune) and in a little ~~cozy~~ corner
on the edge of where the ~~sand~~
dunes become forest. Then we
set out for the beach. The sky
was blue, the air was perfectly
warm with cool, intermittent breezes
the lake was the perfect temperature
the sand was soft and warm to the

④

touch.... And the flies were
swarming in noxious clouds!
We quickly found that we couldn't
stay in one place for more than
thirty seconds without being
covered by literally hundreds of
little black flies who would
administer painful bites to any
exposed flesh. We huddled
together eating our lunch with
a free hand to swat them away,
and then were forced ~~went~~ into the water,
where they weren't as bad. We
tried, desperately to stick it out,
to cover ourselves, to walk along
the beach, but the flies were
unstoppable, they were indomitable
they were everywhere!
Finally, feeling defeated we left
our stuff and hiked back ~~on~~ to
the car, and drove into town for
some respite.

THE KEYS

YES, we were tired, a tiny bit

miserable, maybe, but the hike
was pleasant enough, and the
town of Luddington was free,
completely liberated, from the
scourge of hell-spawned insects
of the dunes. We were happy. We
found a local brew pub and sat
on their patio (with a gorgeous
view of the... uh... parking lot)
and ate dinner, veggie burgers and
beer. Then we ambled around town
peeking into antique stores, exchanging
friendly hello's with the locals. We
bought ice cream ~~and~~ and ambled
over to the marina, reclining on the
grass and enjoying the continued
absence of flies. We talked for awhile
and then, as the sun just began to
slip ~~past the~~ the horizon we headed
back to the car.

"maybe the flies will go away
~~when~~ when the sun goes down," I
said to cheryl as I fished in
my pocket for the ~~keys so~~ key.

"Gee, I hope so" she said,
as I fished in my other pocket
for the key.

"do you have your key?"

©

I asked Cheryl, as I fished in my back pockets for the key.

"No, you said you had yours so I left mine at the campsite" said Cheryl as I checked my front pockets again, beginning to get worried, "Why?" there was a note of concern, with just a slight tickle of annoyance mixed in for good measure.

"I... uh... I don't seem too... uh" I said as I tried to think what I had done with them, and peer non-chalantly into the car to see if they were in the ignition, And check all the door handles as casually as possible.

"You don't have them?" I checked each of my pockets 7 or 8 ~~more~~ times but came up empty each time. The keys were nowhere to be seen. Slowly the color leached out of both of our faces, as we realized that, if we could not find the key, we would be separated from the only other key, Cheryl's, by miles and miles of ~~could~~ ~~rost~~ circuitous country road ~~probably~~ and a two mile hike. Then, the same trip back. Meanwhile, it was

⑦

getting dark. We probably would
be forced to spend the night in town,
at a motel, and retrieving the
key~~s~~ would probably take all the
next day, Quite effectively ruining
the vacation. ~~Because~~ I was
struck by the enormous absurdity
of the situation and let out a little
laugh. ~~I couldn't~~ Cheryl didn't.
We set about retracing our steps
hoping the sunlight didn't completely
disappear before we finished. The
nice people at the ice cream store
looked at me like I was crazy.
The tourists by the Marina
licked their ice cream cones
blankly as we frantically combed
through the grass on our hands
and knees, every foil gum wrapper
was like a punch in the face.
Apparently the gods were just playing
with us. They weren't really out
for complete devestation. After
a couple of minutes a little silver
subaru key seemed to levitate
mildly out of the grass with a
little smirk on it's face as if to

⑧

say "gee! that was fun, I didn't
think you guys would EVER find me!"
Cheryl and I picked ourselves up
and dusted ourselves off, assured
one another that we ~~had known~~ we'd find
it all along, and ~~walked~~ walked
back to the car, just as the sun
went down over the lake.

THE FLASHLIGHT BATTERIES

The route back to the parking-lot-
in-the-woods looked different in
the dark, but we made it with no
wrong turns. We parked and fished
out the flashlight, which we had
fortunately had the forsight to bring
along, knowing getting through the
twisty, maze like path in the dark
would be hard enough even with the
flashlight. About ten minutes into
the 40-60 minute walk, the batteries
went dead.
     "Anders -- what are you doing?"
     "The... uh... The batteries... uh"
     click click

There wasn't actually a moon
out yet, it wouldn't show itself
for another hour or so, but the
sky wasn't ~~light~~ completely dark.
The situation was helped by the fact
that the path was, in most places,
made of sand, which was much
lighter in color than the surrounding
forest floor. (Cheryl felt like someone
had locked her in a closet, she couldn't
see a thing. But I could make out
just enough that, leading her ~~through you~~ on
the path by her hand we made
slow progress. We both were swatted in the face
with a few branches, and once, in
a place ~~where~~ fallen trees lay accross
the path, ~~she got a painful~~ Cheryl
got a painful jab in the leg from
a pointy branch. (a very beautiful
red scratch surrounded by a little
purple ring). ~~and~~ Eventually we
made it out into the open air
the tent, and then back down to
the beach to enjoy the stars. The
bugs had indeed disappeared the
cold and the dark (or at least
the dark, as we shall see later), they

(10)

didn't seem to mind cold.) had driven
them home to sleep. The incredible
dome of stars (remember we come from
Chicago - there aren't really any stars
there) the pleasant air, the solitude,
it all made the trip seem just fine,
all the little troubles receded, began
to seem silly, comical. It was really
beautiful. After a little while we
climbed back over the dunes, went
into the tent, cuddled up and drifted
off to ~~a welcome~~ a welcome sleep.

THE RACCOONS

Soon, maybe a half hour had
passed, I awoke. I'd had some dream
involving a friend who was getting
too close, taking something. But what
awakened me was actually the sound
of scratching, of snuffling outside.
Then someone started eating cornchips.
  "crunch, crunch. chomp chomp chomp"
  ~~chomp~~ This woke Cheryl
  "What are you doing?" she asked me.
  ~~illegible crossed out~~

⑪

The chewing stopped.

"I think we have some friends" I said.

The chewing started up again

"chomp chomp chomp"

pause

"chomp chomp chomp"

it was funny. but it was also loud and we were tired. I had a vague memory of laying a bag of corn chips by the tent before going down to the lake earlier in the day. and I was reasonably sure that the sounds were of a small animal, not, like, a bear or something. reasonably sure.

"what are we going to do?"

"I don't know what should we do?"

"I don't know. You don't think it's, like, a bear or something"

"well we can't just lay here and listen it's going to drive me crazy"

"crunch crunch crunch"

pause

"crunch crunch crunch"

⑫

"okay" I said trying to sound brave and resolute "I'm going to go out and get rid of the chips." I started rolling up the sleeping mat to use as a weapon. I figured I'd come out swinging and scare it away long enough to grab the chips. and bring them back inside, or toss them away or something. my plan was pretty vague

"Here goes" I unzipped the tent and squeezed out as quickly as possible, also trying to swing the sleeping mat in the general direction of the crunching. I thought I heard some sort of scurrying away sound, and sure enough the silhouette of a raccoon appeared against the sky on a little ridge about twelve feet away. He sat there watching me. I heard more scampering away to my left.

"There's more than one" I said still trying to sound casual and resolute, although the thought

of fending off two (or three
or four) sets of teeth and claws
in the pitch black, coming from
two directions was, well, unsettling.
   I felt around the corner of
the tent where the sound had come
from.

   "what's happening" said cheryl.
I wasn't finding any chips
   "I don't..." then my hand
went under the tent. ~~There were~~
~~a few chips but only crumbs.~~
there was a" hole, in the fabric just big enough
for my hand to go in. ~~Inside the~~
<u>inside</u> the tent, about six inches
from where my head would have
been, I found the bag of chips,
shredded, chips all over. I tried
to ~~protect~~ keep my voice calm
and casual

   "Cheryl... The chips are,...
INSIDE the tent!"

   "WHAT!? WHAT!?"
It took me a moment to realize
that in her mind that meant
the ~~raccoons~~ raccoons were in there too.
I reassured her she was alone.

(14)

21

The raccoon on the ridge
shifted, still watching me.
~~My attempt to party read that~~
~~and he spotted my idea was meant to~~
This, of course, meant that
we couldn't really sleep there.
~~Well for nothing~~ I started
pulling the chips out of the hole
and stuffing them into our little
cooler (which had also, brilliantly,
been left outside) ~~the rest~~ what
didn't fit I stuffed into the
torn up bag and tossed over
the banking, as far from the
tent as possible. There also
happened to be several nectarines
and pears in the tent, these
also, Cheryl passed through the
hole. I threw them, as hard
as I could, and as accurately
as I could in the dark AT the
raccoon and over the banking.
a couple came within inches, but
he was completely unfazed. He
kept watching me. I heard more
shuffling to my left
         We got all the food out,

pulling it through the hole with
one hand, and brandishing the
sleeping mat with the other
and then we had no choice but
to pack up and go find a place
on the beach. You might think
hiking out to the car and
leaving the whole mess behind
would be another possibility. But
you have to remember we had
no flashlight and the hike in in
the dark had been hard enough
without our huge backpacks. So
we collected our blankets, double
checked that there was no food
in the tent and headed back out
to the beach. Rationally, I suppose,
one could reason that once the
food was out, the raccoons would
leave us alone. But ~~there~~ there were
residual smells, and that hole, and
I'll be damned if I'm ever going
to risk being cornered in a
little two person tent with
two (or three or four) hungry
raccoons... ~~and that~~ in the forest,
in the dark.

⑯

The COLD, THE HARD SAND
AND THE RETURN OF THE SWARM

the idea of sleeping on the
beach under the stars, with the
sound of waves gently lapping
the shore... this is a pleasant,
romantic idea. And indeed, for
about, oh, forty five minutes,
maybe an hour, aside from
~~each little sound in the grass~~
~~jerking so awake be~~
being jerked awake by each
sound in the grass that could
have been a raccoon... ASIDE from
that, it was very pleasant and
romantic. But forty five minutes
or an hour passes quickly when
you're feeling pleasant and romantic.
and then the sand gets hard. And
cold. And pretty soon there's
not nearly enough blanket, you
feel like your trying to cover
yourselves with a ~~something~~
piece of typing paper. Which
isn't much even if you don't have
to share it. As it was any
movement AT ALL ~~and~~ was a

(17)

potential danger to blanket
coverage. So moving was out ~~and~~ of the question
and it got colder... and colder... and
the sand got harder.... and
harder. And the little intervals
of sleep between cold hand
~~cold~~ bleary-eyed waking got
shorter... and shorter. Periodically
I would wake and stretch my head
east, carefully - to avoid disturbing the
~~blanket~~ blanket - to see if the sun was
considering showing itself. Finally,
after the longest four or five
hours of my life, a little ~~warm~~ light
seemed to show itself, It peaked
gently ~~*~~ into the dark purple, tinging
it ever lighter shades of blue.

Shortly after that, the flies
too, began to peak gently under the
blanket. staying covered with the
blanket became even more of a
priority, as any exposed skin would
~~let in col~~ now get bitten as well
as let in the cold.

~~One would imagine if given the choice, that~~

With the light and the bugs sleep had
become less desireable as well as
barely possible. We lay there
⑱

for a little while, giggling about
our predicament, it's absurdity, the
intense relief of the morning light
the flies, the flashlight, the corn chip
munching raccoons, the stiffness of
our backs. It all seemed incredibly
hilarious once the sun was, up, or
definately on it's way. At a
few minutes after 5:00 am we
got up, packed the wounded tent
and hiked slowly out.

The morning in town was
very nice. We had breakfast in
a patched together little diner, filled
with locals, went for a walk along
the pier, out to an old lighthouse
with graffiti scratched in the
waterproofing around the base, and
went for one of the most
pleasant swims I've ever swam
in the lake. The sun was warm
there were no flies or raccoons.
it was perfect. Then we lay
down on the beach and slept.
(I was fully clothed — fearing
sun burn... I'm sure we looked to

⑲

the locals like a couple of drunks,
crashed out, fully clothed, on a blanket
on the beach at eight in the morning.
   After that everything else about
the trip went fine. Cheryl did get a
little rash from slathering on too much
bug spray -- possibly exacerbated by the
somewhat stressful circumstances. We
took back roads part of the way home
stopping to get some locally grown
peaches and blueberries, and again to
have ~~coffee and~~ ice cream and coffee
(for some reason we were having trouble
staying awake. The gods did get in
one final laugh. When we got home
we found that the circuit breaker that
powers our refridgevator ~~was~~ had
been tripped. The fridge was warm
and smelly. And a few things had to
get tossed. But we didn't care. We
were happy to be home. We walked to
a nearby cafe, exclaiming all the
way our profound appreciation for
city life... sidewalks, streetlights,
loud puerto ricans having barbecues
(scaring away raccoons) houses, beds
Our next camping trip, we decided, will
include a hotel room.
(20)

So, my dear sister, that's the story of our camping trip. I hope it was a little bit entertaining. Please tell Cici and your mom and dad Hello, and give everyone a big hug I wish I could be there with you all. but I guess it will happen later in the summer. til then,

much love,
Anders

3. New Jersey

4.a. Journal Entry, 01.03.05-01.05.05

4.b. List of Things, in Spite of which, She
Will Probably Marry Him Anyway

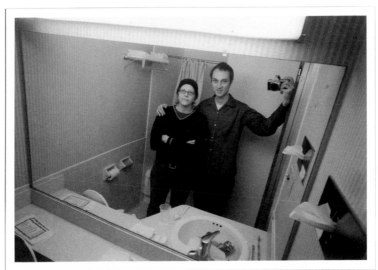

THESE ARE A COUPLE OF PICTURES OF THE MOTEL ROOM
AND CINAPLEX PARKING LOT OF PHILLIPSBURG, NEW JERSEY,
WHERE CHERYL AND I SPENT CHRISTMAS, 2003, AFTER SHE
FELL ASLEEP AT THE WHEEL, LEAVING US STRANDED WITH
A BENT AXLE. IT WAS ACTUALLY A VERY PLEASANT
CHRISTMAS.

I'M GRUMPY. BAD MOOD.

feeling better. hope this notebook holds together.
sitting at filter, waiting for Cheryl to get a
massage from Becca down the street. Cheryl and
I reserved a venue - promontory point - to
get married September 18th. funny.

THINGS HE DOES, IN SPITE OF
WHICH, SHE WILL PROBABLY MARRY
HIM ANYWAY

- FORGETS TO CLOSE CUPBOARDS
- LEAVES DIRTY WATER IN DISHPAN, ALSO ONE KNIFE/FORK
- LEAVES BATHROOM MAT ON FLOOR AFTER SHOWER

- LEAVES MILK OUT
- LEAVES TOP OFF OF ALMOND JAR
- LEAVES BAG OF CHIPS OPEN SO THEY GET STALE

- NOT VERY GOOD AT COLLABORATION ON
    ART PROJECTS. UNCOMPROMISING

- USES TOO MANY DISHES WHEN MAKING DINNER

- FORGETS TO SQUEEZE OUT SPONGES, SO THEY
    SMELL MILDEWY

- MAKES BED INCORRECTLY

- SUCKS TEETH (RECENT DEVELOPMENT)

- NEGLECTS TO CLIP NAILS

5. Getting to France

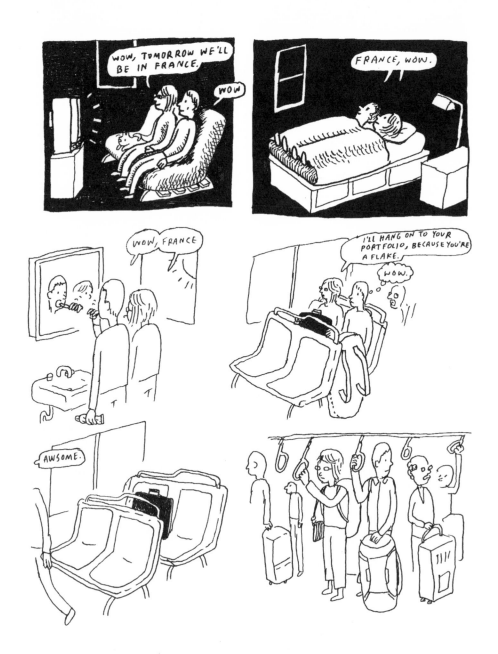

6. France

WE DID FINALLY GET TO FRANCE. WE STAYED IN BORDEAUX AND SPLIT
A RENTAL CAR WITH ALVIN AND KEVIN TO GET TO ANGOULEME EACH
DAY. BORDEUX WAS NICE. THE MAIN COMMERCIAL STREETS IN THE
CENTER OF THE CITY ARE ALL PEDESTRIAN ONLY. IT'S ODD TO
HEAR THE NORMAL NOISE AND CHAOS OF THE CITY... MINUS THE
SOUND OF TRAFFIC. IT'S VERY QUIET AND HUMAN.

THIS WINDOW FACED OUT ON A TRAFFIC CIRCLE AT THE END OF OUR
STREET. IT'S ALL FOIS GRAS -- LIVERS OF FORCE-FED GEESE. AFTER
WE TOOK THE PICTURE THE WOMAN CAME OUT, SAID SOMETHING
IN FRENCH, AND GLARED AT US.

THIS IS A MONUMENT TO THE FRENCH REVOLUTION. DURING THE
WAR AND OCCUPATION IT WAS DISMANTLED BY THE CITIZENS AND
HIDDEN IN PEOPLES HOMES TO SAVE IT FROM BEING MELTED DOWN
BY THE GERMANS.

FRENCH DUCKS ARE DIFFERENT THAN AMERICAN DUCKS

CHERYL READING IN OUR HOTEL ROOM.

I DON'T KNOW WHAT HAPPENED HERE, BUT IT'S PROBABLY THE BEST PICTURE WE GOT OF THE CITY.

THERE'S SOMETHING REALLY NICE ABOUT THE COMBINATION OF THE ANCIENT AND THE POST-MODERN

CHERYL TRYING TO FIGURE OUT WHERE WE'RE GOING.
THE STEPS BEHIND HER WOULD BE A NICE MANUAL PAD.*

THIS BENCH WOULD BE PRETTY GOOD TOO. AND THE GROUND IS
SUPER SMOOTH STONE.

*FOR SKATEBOARDING.

CHERYL THOUGHT I LOOKED LIKE THIS GUY.

IN FRANCE, EVEN THE TRAFFIC MARKINGS ARE
BEAUTIFULLY DESIGNED.

CUT-OUT SILHOUETTES LIKE THE ONE ON THE RIGHT
WERE A REGULAR FEATURE OF THE LANDSCAPE ALONG THE
ROAD. PRESUMABLY THEY MARK THE SITE OF A FATALITY.

THE COMICS FESTIVAL IS HELD IN THE OLD CITY IN ANGOULEME,
AT THE TOP OF A HILL WITH GREAT VIEWS. I DIDN'T GET ANY
GOOD PICTURES OF THEM.

THE FRONT OF ANGOULEME'S CATHEDRAL
PUT A LOT OF THE COMICS TO SHAME.

THE STREETS WERE PACKED WITH COMIC FANS.

OUR BOOTH (AND PAUL)

A TWO-LEGGED HORSE BALLOON

A DAY AFTER THE SHOW ENDED, WE TOOK A TRAIN TO ARCACHON, A LITTLE RESORT TOWN ON THE COAST. BEING THE MIDDLE OF WINTER, IT WAS CLOSED DOWN. MOST OF THE HOUSES WERE BOARDED UP AND THE STREETS WERE DESERTED.

THE FEW STORES THAT WEREN'T CLOSED FOR THE
SEASON **WERE** CLOSED FOR MOST OF THE TIME WE
WERE THERE. THE ONLY FOOD WE COULD FIND, AFTER
A LONG SEARCH, WERE SOME CROISSANTS AND
COFFEE, WHICH WE ATE WHILE WE WAITED FOR THE
TRAIN BACK TO BORDEAUX.

5. The Hospital

so... spending the day at the hospital, cook county
with Cheryl. Yesterday her doctor (sheila) ~~at~~
st Elizabeths said she thought she had
non-hodgkins Lymphoma. today this guy Dr. Kevy (?)
thinks she may need a spleen-ectomy. It's all
a bit too much. not _too_ much. just a lot.
I may not fly out to S.F. for APE on
Friday, we'll see. Cheryl seems to want me
to go. I think I'll feel bad if I go. I feel
like I should be here. with her, just making
sure things are okay, available to look after
her. On the other hand It's worth about,
oh, $600 or more for me to go, and money's
going to be tight for awhile regarding her
being Ill and not working.

We got here just before 7:00 am
today. now it's 11:20. I'm sitting in the
car, chilling out for a bit, though in a minute
I'm going to go see if I can find A) Lunch,
B) a walkman w/ radio for her in case she ~~~~
has to stay here overnight.
It's a strange thing.

sitting at the hospital at cook county, today is cheryl's
first day of CHEMO. We got here at 7:30 or 8:00 am,
it's now approaching 1:30pm. I just left a few minutes
ago to come down here to the cafeteria to have lunch
and take it easy. It's really too much. both of us are
stressed out and don't know what to do. I don't know
if I should... A, B, C. anything. Do less of my own work
and instead..... do more research about stuff... I don't know
how can I help her? I have no idea. She made
a comment the other day about she guesses ~~you~~ you
go through it alone, ultimately, no matter what. and I
don't know if that was just an observation of
the simple facts - there certainly is a very real
way in which that's true. I can't know what it's
like. The enlarged spleen ~~not~~ will never be completely
real to me, the weight she's lost, the short hair
cut she was compelled to get... the weird revelation
these kinds of things entail that "THIS IS HAPPENING

63

TO ME." repeated over and over ✪ "I HAVE CANCER. THIS
IS HAPPENING TO ME." how do I help? how would I want
her to help if it was reversed? ~~is~~ is that applicable
even, or is she just too different from me, different
needs, desires, priorities, concerns... none of it feels real to
me at all. It's just like a series of doctors appointments
a lot of waiting in lobbies. vague uncertainty and lack
of control. These are new for me, at least in there
immediacy. Is it rude to cheryl for me to read the
New Yorker instead of... what, talking to her? trying to
calm her? would these help?
especially when I'm so aware
lately of getting on her nerves.

10·12·05

Sitting in the hospital with cheryl. she had
chest pains last night at about 1:30 and we
came to the ER. It's now 18:55. Still waiting for a
bed. waiting waiting waiting. so much to do, so much to
attend to, but I'm sitting in the hospital waiting. at least I got
to go home and sleep for a little bit. cheryl hasn't slept for
about thirty four hours or something.

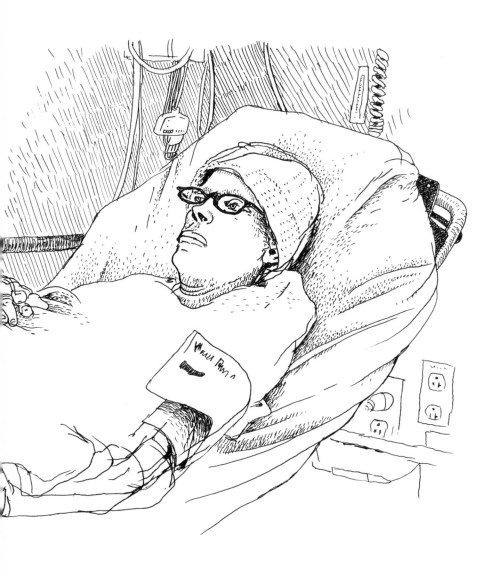

CHERYL IN E.R. ISOLATION UNIT 10-12-05

cheryl is sleeping. It's Sunday afternoon now. she's still in the hospital, but upstairs now, in 7 west, room 7533, I think. there are so many things swirling in my head, in my life. Theres a weird disconnect... In one way it doesn't seem like all of this is, or should be that hard. I come here and sit with her, read to her, get her some food, watch the game, then I go home and eat, sleep, work on the cover for Hans Christian andersen's Fairy tales... why should that be so hard? why should I have a hard time getting up in the morning, or start crying while talking to my sister on the phone, or while driving to the hospital? I mean, of course it _is_ hard. it's emotionally... draining, frustrating etc. it's just too much. but it's also just very plain and boring. mundane. drudgery. It's not like running a

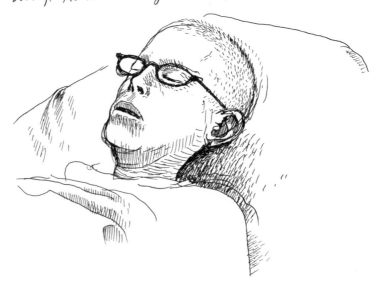

marathon or lifting weights. It's not like taking calculus, but forgetting to study. It's just hard. In its own way. It occured to me on the way over that I can't really go in to Lula because it's too hard. everyone asks how cheryl is and how I am and it's a little too much to handle. the last time I went I almost broke down in tears when Natalie put her hand around me. All of this is making me a little fragile. making the shell, the membrane between normalcy and collapse very very thin.

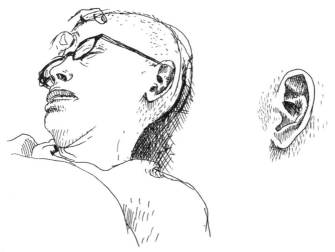

Cheryl is sleeping right now. The artery in her neck is pumping and bounding vigorously, her mouth is open, teeth apart. The I.V. pump hums and clicks softly, intermittently it's gray outside. from up here the brick houses and

apartment buildings are all flattened against the earth. There
is so much room we don't take up. room for the occasional
bird to fly through lazily, and for the clouds to just sit there
filtering light.

NOVEMBER 7<u>th</u> (?... it's MONDAY)

been a rough several days... the worst so far I
think - cheryl completely exhausted, in a daze, confused, delirious...
she understands what you say and can respond but says
other oddball things as well. Asked about when they
were going to come back to "SHOOT THE EGG" meaning
tap her belly for fluid - aceites (?) referred to herself
with OGUNDIPE, as "~~put~~ "PUSHED AROUND, LIKE A CHICKEN"
something about being a "HOLIDAY BIRD" AND BEING
"HERDED WITH SHEEP" but she knew what day of the week
it was, where she is, and who I am.

FAIRNESS IS A HUMAN DELUSION

WHAT DO YOU SAY TO SOMEONE WHEN
THEY ASK YOU "AM I GOING TO DIE?"
AND YOU KIND OF THINK THEY MIGHT,
BUT THERE'S NO WAY TO KNOW, AND
YOU DON'T WANT TO UPSET THEM

AT LEAST, AT THE MOMENT, SHE IS ASLEEP.

I WILL BE SO THANKFUL IF THIS ALL TURNS OUT
FOR THE BEST.

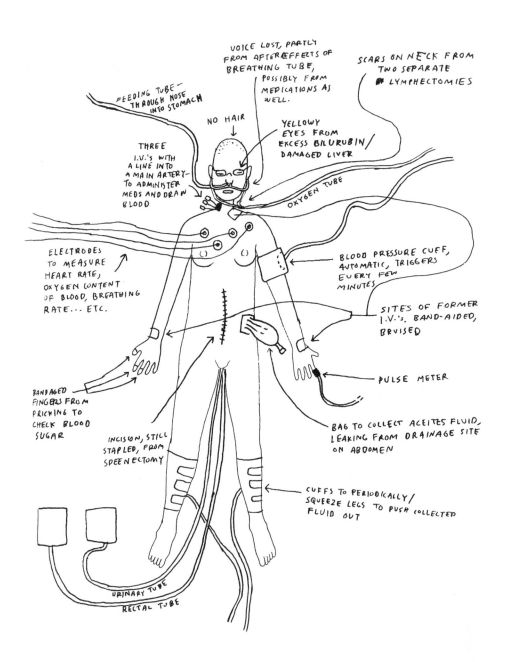

VOICE LOST, PARTLY
FROM AFTEREFFECTS OF
BREATHING TUBE,
POSSIBLY FROM
MEDICATIONS AS
WELL.

SCARS ON NECK FROM
TWO SEPARATE
LYMPHECTOMIES

FEEDING TUBE-
THROUGH NOSE
INTO STOMACH

NO HAIR

YELLOWY
EYES FROM
EXCESS BILIRUBIN/
DAMAGED LIVER

THREE
I.V.'s WITH
A LINE INTO
A MAIN ARTERY
TO ADMINISTER
MEDS AND DRAW
BLOOD

OXYGEN TUBE

ELECTRODES
TO MEASURE
HEART RATE,
OXYGEN CONTENT
OF BLOOD, BREATHING
RATE... ETC.

BLOOD PRESSURE CUFF,
AUTOMATIC, TRIGGERS
EVERY FEW
MINUTES

SITES OF FORMER
I.V.'s BAND-AIDED,
BRUISED

BANDAGED
FINGERS FROM
PRICKING TO
CHECK BLOOD
SUGAR

PULSE METER

INCISION, STILL
STAPLED, FROM
SPLEENECTOMY

BAG TO COLLECT ACEITES FLUID,
LEAKING FROM DRAINAGE SITE
ON ABDOMEN

CUFFS TO PERIODICALLY/
SQUEEZE LEGS TO PUSH COLLECTED
FLUID OUT

URINARY TUBE
RECTAL TUBE

70

Express yourself completely,
then keep quiet.
Be like the forces of nature:
when it blows, there is only wind;
when it rains, there is only rain;
when the clouds pass, the sun shines through.

If you open yourself to the WORLD
you are at one with the WORLD
and you can embody it completely.
If you open yourself to insight,
you are at one with insight
and you can use it completely.
If you open yourself to loss,
you are at one with loss
and you can accept it completely.

The path into the light seems dark,
the path forward seems to go back,
the direct path seems long,
true power seems weak,
true purity seems tarnished,
true steadfastness seems changeable,
true clarity seems obscure,
the greatest art seems unsophisticated,
the greatest love seems indifferent,
the greatest wisdom seems childish.

Be content with what you have;
rejoice in the way things are.
When you realize there is nothing lacking,
the whole world belongs to you.

6. The Lake

CHERYL, THIS IS ON THE WAY TO PROMONTORY POINT AFTER SETTING THINGS UP AT THE CHURCH. I DON'T REMEMBER FOR SURE WHO WAS WITH ME. I THINK ADAM. PROBABLY MY MOM. WHEN WE STARTED OUT EVERYONE WAS BEHIND ME, FOLLOWING. I STOPPED FOR A WHILE AND LET THEM PASS. YOU ARE IN MY ARMS.

THIS IS THE BRIDGE UNDER LAKE SHORE DRIVE AND INTO PROMONTORY POINT. IT'S LIKE A PASSAGEWAY FROM THE UNIVERSITY, THE SHOPS, NORMAL LIFE, TO THE EDGE OF THE WATER, TO WHERE WE WERE GOING TO BE MARRIED. WHERE WE USED TO TAKE THOSE LONG WALKS WHEN WE WERE JUST GETTING TO KNOW ONE ANOTHER.

COMING OUT OF THE TUNNEL THE FIELD SPREADS OUT SUDDENLY, LIKE TAKING A DEEP BREATH. COMING OVER THE HILL WE SEE A CROWD OF PEOPLE. THERE ARE A LOT OF THEM. I DON'T KNOW IF WE COULD HAVE HAD THAT SMALL WEDDING WE TALKED ABOUT. WHO'S HERE? EVERYONE. BOTH OUR FAMILIES. FRIENDS. EVERYONE.

THAT'S AARON OTT, FROM FLATFILE. THAT'S LE VU. CAN YOU BELIEVE THAT? SHE'D NEVER MET YOU AND SHE CAME ALL THE WAY FROM SAN FRANCISCO. WITH HER BABY. CLARA PRESLER WAS THERE. EVERYONE FROM LULA. EVERYONE FROM MK. JOHNNY AND BRENDAN CAME FROM NEW YORK, EMILY AND ADAM... CAMERON CAME BACK FROM NEW ORLEANS.

I THINK YOU WOULDN'T HAVE LIKED THIS VERY MUCH, TO HAVE BEEN THERE. EVERYONE FUSSING OVER YOU. IT WOULD HAVE DRIVEN YOU NUTS. YOU'D HAVE WANTED TO GO HOME AND GET SOME WORK DONE. I THINK YOU MIGHT HAVE LIKED WATCHING IT, THOUGH. HOVERING ABOVE IT. IT PROBABLY MADE YOU SAD, BUT I DON'T THINK EVEN YOU COULD HAVE QUESTIONED IT. YOU MADE PEOPLE FEEL AT HOME IT THE WORLD. EVEN PEOPLE YOU BARELY KNEW. EVEN THOUGH YOU NEVER REALLY FELT THAT WAY YOURSELF.

DID YOU KNOW AMY'S WATER BROKE AT THE CEREMONY? WHILE I WAS DOWN BY THE WATER SCATTERING YOUR ASHES, HER WATER BROKE. SHE GAVE BIRTH LATER THAT NIGHT. SPOOKY, HUH? DID YOU HAVE A HAND IN THAT? IT DOESN'T SEEM LIKE YOUR STYLE, BUT THAT LAST WEEK IN THE HOSPITAL YOU WERE DEVELOPING A GOOFY SENSE OF HUMOR. SO MAYBE IT WAS YOU. OR MAYBE SOMEONE DID IT ON YOUR BEHALF. HE'S A VERY CUTE KID, ALVA. I JUST MET HIM A COUPLE OF WEEKS AGO, WHEN YOUR PARENTS WERE IN TOWN, AT LULA.

SO, THAT'S ME, DOWN BELOW, TO SCATTER YOUR ASHES | SLIPPED ON THE ROCKS ONCE, AND ALMOST WENT INTO THE WATER.

PAUL KEPT TELLING ME NOT TO BE DISSAPOINTED, THAT THESE THINGS NEVER HAPPEN EXACTLY HOW YOU EXPECT. THE WIND WILL SHIFT, THE ASHES WILL BLOW IN YOUR FACE. BUT IT DIDN'T. IT WENT PERFECTLY. YOUR ASHES SCATTERED PERFECTLY, DISSOLVING INTO A CREAMY WHITE CLOUD IN THE WATER, DRIFTING DOWN AMONG THE ROCKS.

I WAS SO SURPRISED THAT THAT WAS WHERE YOU SAID YOU WANTED THEM TO GO. MAYBE YOU FELT MORE AT HOME HERE, IN CHICAGO, IN THE MIDWEST, WITH ME THAN I THOUGHT. MAYBE MORE THAN **YOU** THOUGHT.

WHEN THE BAG WAS EMPTY I JUST WANTED TO SIT AND SOB AND COLLAPSE INTO THE WATER WITH YOU AND DISAPPEAR. THAT FEELING LASTED FOR MANY DAYS. BUT I DIDN'T COLLAPSE. I GOT UP AND WENT BACK UP ONTO THE GRASS. GOT HUGS. CRIED SOME MORE AND WALKED BACK. LATER ELLA SANG FOR YOU, JIM AND LEA AND MIKE PLAYED SOME ELIZABETH COTTON SONGS. PEOPLE SAID A LOT OF NICE THINGS.

THERE'S MORE, MY DEAR. MORE THAN COULD FIT IN ONE LITTLE LETTER, ONE CONVERSATION OR A THOUSAND. THERE IS EVERYTHING THAT HAS HAPPENED IN THE LAST TWO MONTHS AND EVERYTHING THAT HASN'T HAPPENED. ANNA AND KATHY CAME. IT WAS GREAT TO SEE THEM. I HAD COFFEE WITH P.L. LAST WEEK, AND ALSO WITH BECCA. I THINK I'VE BEEN SEEKING ILLUMINATION FROM SOME OF THESE PEOPLE, AND I GUESS I'VE FOUND SOME, BUT YOU WERE A PUZZLE TO EVERYONE. WHICH IS AT LEAST IN PART WHY WE ALL LOVED YOU SO MUCH. REALLY, WE DID. EVERYONE. AND JUST SO YOU KNOW, I FORGIVE YOU FOR EVERYTHING. I HOPE YOU CAN FORGIVE ME. AS WE'VE FOUND OUT, AS WE'VE BEEN MADE SO TERRIBLY AWARE BY ALL OF THIS, WE'RE HUMAN. I MISS YOU, BABE.

7. Postcards from him to her

THE PIGEONS IN ~~DETROIT EI~~ WASHINGTON LOOK EXACTLY LIKE THE ONES IN CHICAGO. ONLY MAYBE A LITTLE MORE GOVERNMENTAL

WE MUST SAVE MEDICARE.

THIS IS THE EAR OF A SMALL FUZZY GREY DOG THAT WAS SITTING AT THE FEET OF A POLICEMAN OUTSIDE FARLEYS COFFEE SHOP IN SAN FRANCISCO. IT STAYED IN THE SAME SPOT, NOT MOVING FOR 20 MINUTES. THEN I DREW THE EAR AND IT GOT UP AND LEFT.

Dear Cheryl,

In sixty years from
now, when I'm on my
deathbed dying (before you,
because youre a smoker
and smokers always outlast
people like me with healthy
habits) and you come
up to our room just before
I croak, I'm going to
say "I told you so."
because we've been in love
all that time and been
having great sex (except
for the last year because I
had been ill) and been happy

And then I'm going to croak
and your going to go back
out to the garden because
after being with me so
long you'll have got
forgetful like me and you'll
forget to call the undertaker.
and you won't be sad.
Because we ~~had~~
such a good life together.

AFTERWORD

IN LATE MARCH OF 2005 MY GIRLFRIEND, CHERYL (BY THEN MY FIANCE, THOUGH SHE HATED THAT WORD) WAS DIAGNOSED WITH CANCER, ULTIMATELY HODGKINS DISEASE. THE PROGNOSIS, FROM THE BEGINNING WAS POSITIVE. THE DOCTORS GAVE HER AN EIGHTY-FIVE PERCENT CHANCE. THERE WAS SOME TALK OF TAKING OUT HER SPLEEN — WHERE THE DISEASE SEEMED TO BE CONCENTRATED, BUT GIVEN THE RELATIVE RISK OF SURGERY AND THE LIKELY-HOOD OF TREATMENT BEING SUCCESSFUL, SURGERY WAS PUT OFF. THINGS DIDN'T TURN AROUND, THOUGH. THE SPLEEN DIDN'T RESPOND AND BY OCTOBER THE CANCER HAD SPREAD TO HER LIVER AND THE PROGNOSIS WAS SUDDENLY DIRE. HER SPLEEN WAS FINALLY REMOVED IN NOVEMBER, BUT HER LIVER WAS FILLED, BY THEN, WITH CANCER. SHE DIED ON THE 13th, HAVING LASTED A LOT LONGER THAN ANYONE HAD EXPECTED A COUPLE OF WEEKS EARLIER.

I COULDN'T REALLY WORK ON ANYTHING ELSE FOR A COUPLE OF MONTHS AFTERWARDS. I COULDN'T THINK ABOUT MUCH ELSE. AND DIDN'T REALLY WANT TO.

I'D INTENDED, BEFORE THE SERIOUSNESS OF CHERYL'S ILLNESS WAS CLEAR, TO DO A SMALL BOOK WITH SOME OF THIS MATERIAL, FOR FRIENDS AND FAMILY CHERYL AND I ALWAYS HAD MINOR DISASTERS WHEN WE TRAVELLED TOGETHER (IN FAIRNESS, I HAD THIS PROBLEM LONG BEFORE I MET HER, BUT IT CONTINUED. SHE BECAME A PARTICIPANT AND, ONLY OCCASIONALLY, A CONTRIBUTOR).

SO THE BOOK IS A COLLECTION OF TRAVEL STORIES, OF TRIPS WE WENT ON TOGETHER, LITERAL OR FIGURATIVE, AND SOME WE WENT ON SEPARATELY, CORRESPONDENCE WHEN WE WERE SEPARATED AND OF DISASTERS, BOTH MINOR AND GREAT AND IRREVOCABLE.

THE POSTCARDS AT THE BEGINNING ARE ONES SHE SENT ME. THOSE AT THE END ARE ONES I SENT HER, BOTH EARLY ON IN THE RELATIONSHIP. ADDED IN ARE A COUPLE OF OTHER LITTLE NOTES AND GIFTS WE LEFT FOR ONE ANOTHER EARLY ON.

THE ACCOUNT OF THE CAMPING TRIP IS A LETTER I WROTE TO MY LITTLE SISTER, A CONNOISEUR OF COMEDY, AFTER THE EVENT. EVERYTHING HAPPENED AS DESCRIBED.

THE PHOTOJOURNAL OF OUR TRIP TO FRANCE IS A SIMPLE RECORD OF OUR EXISTING IN THE WORLD TOGETHER. OF WALKING AROUND, LOOKING. THE BLACK AND WHITE PICTURES WERE NOT INTENDED TO BE, OR TO SEEM, POIGNANT. THAT WAS SIMPLY THE ROLL OF FILM THAT WAS IN THE CAMERA THAT DAY. THE TWO DOUBLE PORTRAITS ARE MY FAVORITE PICTURES OF HER THAT I HAVE NOW. THAT TRIP ALSO MARKS THE END OF NORMAL. SHE WAS ALREADY FEELING WHAT SEEMED THEN LIKE MYSTERIOUS, DISCONNECTED SYMPTOMS, BUT THEY WERE STILL PRETTY EASY TO IGNORE.

AS FOR AIR FRANCE -- WE WERE ABLE TO GET ON A FLIGHT THE NEXT MORNING, SO IT ALL WORKED OUT.

THE ▨ SECTION "THE HOSPITAL" IS WRITING AND A ▨ FEW DRAWINGS I DID OF CHERYL ▨▨▨▨▨▨▨▨▨ MOSTLY IN THE LAST MONTH OR SO. ▨ THE PARKING SITUATION AT THE HOSPITAL WAS VERY BAD. WE HAD TO PARK SEVERAL BLOCKS AWAY USUALLY. THE WALK FROM OUR USUAL SPOT CROSSED A ▨ VACANT LOT, FILLED WITH GRAVEL AND RUBBLE THAT HAD ONCE BEEN PART OF THE MASONRY OF A PREVIOUS BUILDING ON THE SITE. EVEN EARLY ON, THE WALK WAS DIFFICULT FOR CHERYL IN HER WEAKENED, UNSTEADY STATE. LATER, I WOULD DROP HER OFF, PARK MYSELF, AND WALK. IN OUR WALKS THROUGH THIS LOT BOTH OF US NOTICED ONE VARIETY OF MASONRY CHUNK - PAINTED ON THE FACE WITH A CREAMY LIGHT GREEN, SOMETHING VERY CLOSE TO CHERYL'S FAVORITE COLOR. ONE DAY I MADE A POINT OF CHOOSING A COUPLE OF THESE, ONES ▨▨▨ OF A NICE SIZE AND SHAPE. MY INTENT WAS TO PRESENT ONE TO HER ONCE SHE WAS WELL, AS A SOUVENIR OF WHAT, WE WERE BOTH SURE, WOULD EVENTUALLY FADE INTO THE PAST AS A TROUBLESOME, ABSURD MEMORY. A BLIP ON THE SCREEN IN OUR LIFE TOGETHER.

FOLLOWING THAT SECTION ARE A COUPLE OF VERSES FROM A TRANSLATION OF THE TAO TE TCHING THAT I CUT UP AND RE-ARRANGED TO READ AT HER MEMORIAL SERVICE.

THE BOOK IS DEDICATED TO CHERYL, IT'S A MEMORIAL TO HER, AND TO HONOR BOTH HER AND OUR LIFE TOGETHER. SHE WAS AMAZING AND WONDERFUL, BRILLIANT, GENEROUS AND COMPLICATED. I AM INCREDIBLY LUCKY TO HAVE HAD THE TIME WITH HER THAT I DID, AS SHORT AS IT SEEMS TO ME NOW.

THE BOOK MUST ALSO BE DEDICATED TO SOME OTHER PEOPLE. OUR FRIENDS AND FAMILY HELPED US IN WAYS THAT HUMBLED ME. WAYS I HAD NO RIGHT TO EXPECT. ▨▨▨▨ IN PARTICULAR I WANT TO ACKNOWLEDGE EVERYONE THAT CAME TO THE HOSPITAL EVERY DAY TO VISIT CHERYL, TO BRING SANDWICHES ▨▨▨, TO TALK... OR JUST TO SIT, JUST SO I KNEW THERE WAS SOMEONE THERE. JASON AND LEA, GERRY, INGRID, TODD AND ASHLEY, JANE, MARIANNE, MOM, ULLA, DICK, MY DAD, ▨▨▨ LILA AND ELLA, SARAH, GABRIEL AND YOSHI AND BECCA. THAT LIST IS, BY NO MEANS, COMPLETE. A LOT OF PEOPLE HELPED IN ALL KINDS OF WAYS AND IT ▨▨▨▨ MAKES ALL THE DIFFERENCE, EVEN NOW. THE BOOK IS ALSO JUST FOR EVERYONE WHO KNEW HER, BUT ESPECIALLY HER FAMILY, JIM, ELVA, JULIE AND CHARLES, STEVEN AND GARY, WHO ALL HELPED US THROUGH AND WHO MISS HER MOST, ALONG WITH ME.

THIS STORY IS, OBVIOUSLY, VERY PERSONAL, BUT ULTIMATELY I THINK IT ISN'T EXCLUSIVE. IT FEELS INCREDIBLY PARTICULAR TO ME, STILL, BUT IT'S JUST LOVE AND LOSS. AND EVERYONE, FOR BETTER OR WORSE, CAN RELATE TO THAT.